The CAPE
FLORAL
KINGDOM

The CAPE FLORAL KINGDOM

Colin Paterson-Jones

First published in 1997 by
New Holland (Publishers) Ltd
London • Cape Town • Sydney • Singapore

24 Nutford Place
London W1H 6DQ
United Kingdom

80 McKenzie Street
Cape Town 8001
South Africa

3/2 Aquatic Drive
Frenchs Forest, NSW 2086
Australia

ISBN 1 85368 481 3

Senior designer: **Trinity Fry**
Editor: **Peter Joyce**
Publishing Manager: **Pippa Parker**
Cartographer: **Desireé Oosterberg**
Proofreader: **Tessa Kennedy**

Reproduction: cmyk pre-press, Cape Town
Printing and binding: Tien Wah Press (Pte) Limited, Singapore

Half title Mimetes hottentoticus flowers high in the southern Hottentots Holland mountains.

Previous page The day-flying heady maiden moth (*Syntomis cerbera*) on a chincherinchee (*Ornithogalum thyrsoides*) flower.

Previous page inset The mountain dahlia (*Liparia splendens*).

Right Mountain fynbos reaches the sea where, above Koeël Bay, *Aulax cancellata* (male) flowers in summer.

CONTENTS

INTRODUCTION

The Cape Floral Kingdom is one of the world's most precious natural assets. So special is the floral wealth on the southern tip of Africa that, as part of the World Wide Fund for Nature's WWF 2000 global conservation campaign, it was identified in 1996 as one of the top twenty among 200 key ecoregions worldwide that are crucial in the drive to conserve nature into the next millennium.

Africa is the cradle of mankind. Fossil records show that Early Stone Age man lived on the southern extremity of the continent for at least 500 000 years. Later came the Bushman (San) hunter-gatherers, who roamed the region from about 21 000 years ago, but sadly we shall never know whether and to what extent they valued its flowers for their beauty: plants are not depicted in their rock art here, and it seems that they did not play a large part in the mystically religious experience, the main subject of the Bushmen's paintings. We do know though, that their more recent relatives, the Khoikhoi pastoralists who brought their flocks of sheep (and, later, herds of cattle) to the south-western and southern Cape about 2 000 years ago, made extensive use of the region's plants for food and medicine.

What has been well recorded is the excitement aroused by the first plants collected and sent to Europe. For more than 150 years, from the time Bartholomeu Dias rounded the Cape in 1488, ships plying the newly charted trade route to the East put ashore on the Cape coast to replenish their water and fresh food supplies. On some of these brief stopovers sailors would collect what to them were strange plants, which they carried back to their home countries. The European Renaissance that spanned the 16th and 17th centuries was a time of discovery, the beginning of the age of scientific enquiry. Rich merchants, members of the nobility and universities created and maintained gardens filled with plants from all over the then known world. Herbalists who studied these living collections and dried material produced books known as 'herbals', in which they described the different species and made the first attempts to understand how they were related. Examples from distant parts of the world were especially prized. The first depiction of a Cape flower – a dry flower-head of *Protea neriifolia* – was in Clusius' *Exoticorum libri decem*, which was published in 1605 in Leiden. Many of the Cape plants featured in the herbals of this time consisted of bulbous species, one of the first of which has been identified as the April fool flower (*Haemanthus coccineus*).

The collecting of Cape plants, even at this early time, was an organized rather than a haphazard process. The wealthy European patrons of the trading expeditions that sailed around the Cape commissioned their ships' captains to gather exotic species, which would later be incorporated into the gardens that were becoming increasingly fashionable and major objects of interest. The establishment of the Dutch

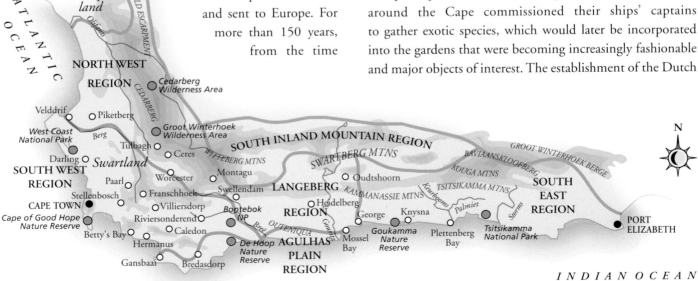

East India Company's settlement at the Cape of Good Hope in 1652 provided the stimulus for even more serious and extensive collecting. So began a tradition of botanical exploration at the Cape which has continued uninterrupted until today.

The most celebrated of the early botanists to come to the Cape was Carl Thunberg, who arrived in April 1772. Thunberg, then 29 years old, was the brilliant student of Carl Linnaeus, the famed Swedish natural scientist who worked at the University of Uppsala. Linnaeus brought order to the rapidly increasing body of knowledge about living organisms and their relationships by introducing the systematic method of naming them that is still used today. According to his binomial system, each species is given a two-part name – for example, *Protea neriifolia*. The second element (*neriifolia*) identifies the species, the first (*Protea*) the name of the genus to which the species belongs. While neither the genus nor the species name is necessarily individually unique, the combination always is. To elaborate: populations of plants which share the same overall characteristics, and which interbreed, form a species. Different species which share one or more specialized characteristics are grouped into a genus. All the species (and, therefore, genera) which share the same basic floral form and structure, or some other uniquely important characteristic, are gathered into one plant family. *Protea neriifolia*, for instance, belongs to the Proteaceae family.

Although nominally an employee of the Dutch East India Company, Thunberg spent his almost three years at the Cape studying and collecting plants, making several expeditions into the interior and along the south coast. He left for Japan in March 1775 to spend a further four years in botanical exploration. Soon after his return to Sweden he took up the chair of

A new *Cyrtanthus* species

botany at Uppsala University, replacing Linnaeus' son (who had briefly succeeded his renowned father). One of the legacies of Thunberg's time at the Cape is his *Flora Capensis*, the first systematic account of the region's plant life. Succeeding generations of botanists added to this monumental work as they searched for, located and recorded more and more of the Cape's abundant plant species.

Today, even after centuries of intensive exploration, the Cape still yields hitherto unknown plants. One of the more noteworthy of the recent discoveries has been *Mimetes chrysanthus,* located in the Gamkaberg Nature Reserve in 1987. An undescribed species of *Cyrtanthus,* which came to light near the pleasant southern Cape town of Swellendam, was only one of several new discoveries made in 1997.

With the accumulation of knowledge came the realization that the Cape Flora is essentially unlike any other elsewhere. So different and varied are the species that grow naturally here that the region has been named the Cape Floral Kingdom, one of only six floristic kingdoms into which the world is divided and enjoying the same status as, for example, the great Boreal Kingdom which covers most of the northern land masses of Europe, Asia and North America – an area of 50 million square kilometres, or 500 times that of the Cape kingdom. About 20 per cent of the over 950 plant genera found here, and a staggering 68 per cent of the more than 8 500 species, are endemic. Equally distinctive are the seven endemic families, namely the Lanariaceae, Stilbaceae, Penaeaceae, Retziaceae, Geissolomaceae, Roridulaceae, and Bruniaceae.

The Proteaceae (restricted to the southern hemisphere), the Mesembryanthemaceae (restricted to Africa), and the Restionaceae (essentially Cape) are among the Cape Flora's ten largest families.

Haemanthus coccineus

Erica taxifolia in the Villiersdorp mountains.

The Cape Flora also boasts a remarkable number of geophytes (that is, plants with bulbs, tubers or corms): the iris family (Iridaceae), for instance, is another of the region's ten most extensive families.

In broad terms, the Cape Floral Kingdom encompasses the mountain ranges that run roughly parallel with the western and southern Cape coasts and the land between them and the sea. It is bordered in the north-west by Namaqualand, inland by the Great Karoo, and in the east by the eastern Cape.

Within this region, the plant life varies greatly. The major vegetation type is fynbos, which covers over 80 per cent of the area. Fynbos is characterized by the dominance of hard-leaved plants and the presence of Cape reeds – species of the Restionaceae – which here take the place of grasses elsewhere as the main understorey component. Also characteristic are shrubs of the protea and erica families (Proteaceae and Ericaceae), although these are not always present.

Fynbos comes in many forms, and one of the reasons for the huge number of species in the Cape Flora is the way this vegetation varies in different habitats. It is the dominant vegetation on both the mountains and the coastal plains, where it generally grows on such nutrient-poor soils as the leached-out white sands that occur here. One specialized type of fynbos grows on the coastal limestone hills, another is found on coastal dunes. Where rainfall is sufficiently high, fynbos will grow on the clay soils of the lower mountain slopes, but these and the flats below them, which have the same shale-derived ground, generally carry a natural vegetation type known as renosterveld. The name comes from the renosterbos (*Elytropappus rhinocerotis*), a shrub with fine, grey leaves and so common that it gives the renosterveld countryside its characteristic, generally drab appearance. First impressions, though, are misleading: renosterveld contains large numbers of uniquely beautiful bulbous plants which are among the glories of the Cape Flora when they flower. Most of them bloom in spring.

The plant species found in fynbos and renosterveld make up most of the Cape Flora but there are other minor vegetation types represented. Temperate forests cover large areas of the southern coastal regions, and there are small patches of forest in wet sites on mountain slopes as far west as Cape Town's Table Mountain. In sharp contrast with the fynbos, though, the forests are poor in species. In the dry valleys between the east-west lying mountain ranges you will find succulent Karoo vegetation, a type characterised by small succulent plants and which is dominant in the Namaqualand

Erica parviflora and *Lonchostoma monogynum* in the Ceres mountains.

Arid fynbos on Gamka Mountain in the Little Karoo.

coastal belt to the north. A thicket type of vegetation called strandveld occurs here and there on limestone soils around the coast. Valley bushveld, a subtropical thicket vegetation, is characteristic of the Eastern Cape, entering the Cape Floral Kingdom at its eastern limits.

The Cape Floral Kingdom is divided into six regions.

The North West region encompasses the Bokkeveld Escarpment and the Matsikamma (which tower grandly above the southern part of Namaqualand's Knersvlakte); the Cedarberg, the Kouebokkeveld, Tulbagh, Ceres and Worcester mountains; Piketberg; and the coastal plain between the Berg and Olifants river mouths.

The South West region covers the whole of the coastal plain south of Piketberg; the Cape Peninsula; the contiguous Bainskloof, Du Toit's Kloof, Franschhoek, Stellenbosch, Villiersdorp and Hottentots Holland mountain ranges; the Worcester-Robertson Karoo; the Riviersonderend range; the Kleinrivier range between Hermanus and Bredasdorp; and Potberg, an isolated mountain on the Agulhas Plain.

The Agulhas Plain stretches from Gansbaai in the west to Mossel Bay in the east, and includes Cape Agulhas, the southernmost tip of Africa.

The South Inland Mountain region contains the Witteberg and Swartberg ranges; the broken range of the Touwsberg, Gamkaberg, Rooiberg and the Kammanassies; and the Little Karoo, the distinctive region that lies between the coastal rampart and the Swartberg to the north.

The Langeberg range of mountains and its forelands comprise the fifth region.

The South East region, which probably has the most varied vegetation of all, includes the southern Cape coast and the unbroken Outeniqua/Tsitsikamma range which lies behind; the Langkloof, Baviaanskloof and the surrounding mountains; and the Groot Winterhoek mountains.

This book illustrates just some of the host of beautiful, rare or interesting plants in the Cape Flora. The choice of species depicted is to some extent personal, has no taxonomic significance and is not representative – many families of the Cape Flora are not featured here. The illustrations are arranged according to the six regions, starting in the north-west, travelling south to the Cape Peninsula, and then eastwards. The flowers from the mountains, the forelands and the coast (if applicable) are grouped within each region. Only some of the species shown are endemic to a particular region, but the forms of more widespread species belong in the sections in which they are illustrated.

Gazania rigens on the rocks near Plettenberg Bay.

THE NORTH WEST

*T*he northern tip of the Cape Floral Kingdom is the Bokkeveld Escarpment, *the northernmost extension of the Table Mountain sandstone (TMS) rock formations which are home to the Cape fynbos. Here, the sandstone lies next to tillite and dolorite rocks more typical of the land to the east and north. The result is an extraordinary concentration of plant species in a limited area. To the south are the Matsikamma and Gifberg massifs, then a vast complex of high, north-south running mountain ranges which reach to Worcester and the Tulbagh valley. All of these, like the isolated Piketberg to the west, are made up mainly of TMS and carry a spectacular array of fynbos species. The shale soils of the lower mountain slopes and adjacent flats used to carry renosterveld rich in bulbous plants, but most of these areas have now been ploughed up.*

The area around Nieuwoudtville is renowned for its spring flower displays, but relatively few people know that some of its autumn flowering plants can be as spectacular. After good autumn rains the candelabra shaped heads of *Brunsvigia bosmaniae* appear in profusion.

Sparaxis pillansii, which is confined to the dolorite rock areas, is one of the Bokkeveld Escarpment's three endemic sparaxis species.

Brunsvigia bosmaniae

Sparaxis pillansii

The satin flower *Romulea monadelpha*

Sparaxis tricolor

Sparaxis elegans and *Sparaxis tricolor*, the Bokkeveld Escarpment area's other two endemics, grow in renosterveld on clay soils. These are the plants that have been used to produce the well-loved sparaxis garden hybrids. *Bulbinella latifolia* var. *doloritica*, as the third part of its name suggests, is confined to dolorite soils and is a Nieuwoudtville endemic, an orange form of the widespread yellow typical form of this species. *Romulea monadelpha* is one of two very similar flowers (the other is *R. sabulosa*), each of which is a local endemic and each distinctively lovely.

< *Sparaxis elegans*

Bulbinella latifolia var. *doloritica*

Wheelflowers *Leucospermum catherinae*

The grey-green leaves of *Leucadendron loranthifolium* are a common sight in the sandy areas of the Olifants River valley near Clanwilliam. The dry fynbos here is atypical in that it includes a variety of annual daisies, which put on a colourful spring show. *Leucospermum catherinae*, one of the pincushions, is found among Table Mountain sandstone rocks in the Cedarberg range, often near a stream.

Leucadendron loranthifolium bushes among spring daisies.

Pelargonium magenteum

Hessea undosa

Hessea undosa is a tiny amaryllid which grows only in mountain seeps. This rare plant flowers briefly, for just one or two weeks, the flowerheads withering before the leaves appear. The sneeublom (*Protea cryophila*) is aptly named as it grows only on the Cedarberg's highest peaks, which lie under snow for long periods in winter. The huge flowerheads are borne at ground level in midsummer. *Pelargonium magenteum* is one of the Cedarberg's showy pelargoniums; *Babiana scabrifolia* is one of its spring-flowering babianas.

The sneeublom *Protea cryophila*

Babiana scabrifolia

Gladiolus comptonii and *G. buckerveldii* are two very local endemics: *G. comptonii* is known only from the top of one of the Cedarberg's western sandstone foothills; *G. buckerveldii* grows under just one or two waterfalls high in the mountains. *Oxalis purpurea* is a common and widespread species. This yellow-flowered form grows in dry clay soils in the Olifants River valley north of the town of Clanwilliam. *Ornithogalum maculatum*, a tiny plant, favours sandstone rock sheets farther south in the same valley.

Gladiolus comptonii

Ornithogalum maculatum

Oxalis purpurea

Gladiolus buckerveldii >

Lachnaea alpina

Agathosma alpina

Lachnaea alpina is one of the showier members of the Thymelaeaceae family, forming a compact shrub found among sandstone rocks high in the Kouebokkeveld mountains. Here you will also see *Agathosma alpina*, which belongs to the Rutaceae family. The leaves of this family's plants produce characteristically pungent smelling oils. The well-known buchu oil comes from two other *Agathosma* species (*A. betulina* and *A. ovata*). *Gethyllis spiralis* is a small summer-flowering amaryllid whose fruits (kukumakranka), like those of other *Gethyllis*, are prized for their scent.

Gethyllis spiralis

Protea laevis

Leucospermum spathulatum

The Kouebokkeveld contains a number of spectacular members of the protea family. *Leucadendron bonum* is an extremely rare, local endemic. Fairly widespread, *Leucospermum spathulatum* sprawls over sandstone rocks. *Protea laevis* is a low-growing plant, found in damp areas, whose large flowerheads are produced at ground level. *Protea effusa* is also a widespread species but this form, with wine-red bracts, is produced on the atypically upright bushes found only in the Kouebokkeveld.

Protea effusa

Leucadendron bonum (male) >

Erica junonia

Erica grandiflora

Erica thunbergii

The Kouebokkeveld is home to a large number of very lovely ericas, including *Erica grandiflora* and *E. irorata*. Perhaps the most spectacular of the Cape Flora's 650 species of *Erica* is the large-flowered form of *Erica junonia*, here shown about twice its actual size. The prize for the most exuberantly coloured erica must surely go to *Erica thunbergii*.

Erica irorata

Micranthus junceus

The Groot Winterhoek Wilderness Area in the Tulbagh mountains is an accessible destination where the plant life is matched only by the magnificent scenery. *Watsonia stokoei*, one of the Iridaceae family, is stimulated to flower in profusion by fire. *Micranthus junceus* belongs to the same family. *Psoralea aphylla* flowers along the many streams which flow through the area.

Psoralea aphylla

Watsonia stokoei

In summer, the streams of the Tulbagh mountains are lined with the flowers of the red disa (*Disa uniflora*). *Gladiolus carneus*, one of the painted lady gladioli, is, like the red disa, very widespread; this form comes from the slopes of the mountains overlooking the Tulbagh valley. This is also the habitat of *Ixia viridiflora*, among the most distinctively coloured species of the Iridaceae. The green ixia, though now rare in its natural habitat, is cultivated the world over. *Lachenalia aloides* is one of the showiest of the genus and comes in many local colour forms; this one grows on the Piketberg.

Lachenalia aloides

The green ixia *Ixia viridiflora*

The painted lady *Gladiolus carneus*

< The red disa *Disa uniflora*, growing along a stream in the Groot Winterhoek Wilderness Area.

The Worcester mountains have a number of endemic plants, among them *Protea holosericea*. Known only from the top of a single peak in the range, the species is related to *Protea magnifica* (see page 60), which is widespread in the Cape Flora and has a number of distinct forms. Another Worcester mountains endemic is *Vexatorella latebrosa*, found on some of the lower southern slopes of the range. The name *Vexatorella* reflects the frustration this plant caused in establishing the taxonomy of the protea family. Only discovered in 1956, by the legendary Miss Elsie Esterhuysen, this puzzling plant had to wait until 1981, when enough flowering material had been collected, before it could be classified. It was clear that the plant did not fit into any of the existing genera of the Proteaceae, so a new genus had to be created.

Gladiolus stefaniae, a magnificent and large gladiolus from the mountains west of Montagu, was thought to be another endemic, but in 1995 a pink-flowered form of this species was found on the Potberg, a long way to the east. The species' curious, broken distribution pattern is typical of several others in the fynbos, something for which there is no satisfactory explanation.

Gladiolus stefaniae

Protea holosericea

Vexatorella latebrosa

Geissorhiza tulbaghensis

Babiana villosa

The renosterveld areas of the North West region are poorly conserved. As a result, once very common spring-flowering bulbs such as the kalkoentjie (*Gladiolus alatus*) and *Babiana villosa*, are far less plentiful now. Because much of their natural habitat has been destroyed by agriculture, *Geissorhiza tulbaghensis* and the largest of the magnificent peacock moraeas, *Moraea gigandra*, are now critically rare and hover on the verge of extinction. The remaining wild plants are threatened by agricultural weedkillers.

< The kalkoentjie *Gladiolus alatus*

Moraea gigandra

Moraea villosa subsp. *villosa*

Moraea neopavonia is another highly threatened renosterveld species. Because of its wider distribution, *Moraea villosa* subsp. *villosa*, a beautiful flower that used to appear in its tens of thousands, can still be found in a few places.

Moraea neopavonia >

THE SOUTH WEST

*T*he South West region is the heart of the Cape Floral Kingdom. It also contains the Cape's greatest concentration of people, and has done for centuries. As a result, many of the lowland and some upland areas have been totally changed from their natural state by agriculture, and by urban and industrial sprawl. Despite this, most of the region's floral treasures are still here and are easily accessible. Their survival has much to do with the mountainous nature of a large part of the terrain, and with the foresight of those people who fought so hard for the creation and maintenance of protected areas such as the Cape of Good Hope Nature Reserve. There are over 2 600 plant species on the Cape Peninsula alone, many of them rare, and many thousands more to be seen in the huge area of mountains inland, along the west coast, and on the few remaining patches of renosterveld.

The Cape west coast is well known for its springtime floral displays. One of the best places to see the flowers is in the West Coast National Park, whose centrepiece is the 16-kilometre long Langebaan lagoon. *Cheiridopsis rostrata* is just one of the many showy plants of this area, usually growing on granite or limestone rocks.

Cheiridopsis rostrata

Spring flowers next to Langebaan lagoon.

Spiloxene capensis

Empodium veratrifolium

Spiloxene capensis and *Empodium veratrifolium* both belong to the Hypoxidaceae family. Spiloxene species flower in spring, empodiums in autumn. *Empodium veratrifolium* grows in the crevices of the granite boulders which are a characteristic feature of the west coast. *Bulbinella elata* enjoys the same microhabitat. *Gethyllis afra,* one of the kukumakrankas, is among the few summer-flowering west coast plants.

Gethyllis afra

Bulbinella elata

Sea lavender *Limonium peregrinum* on the dunes.

Satyrium erectum

Agathosma thymifolia and *Thamnochortus spicigerus*

The muted summer colours of the west coast are enlivened when the sea lavender (*Limonium peregrinum*) flowers. This lovely plant is the most showy of a number of *Limonium* species found in the Cape Floral Kingdom.

Satyrium erectum is one of several spring-flowering orchids which grow on the limestone rocks that are as characteristic a feature of this coast as the granite outcrops.

Agathosma thymifolia is a Cape west coast endemic, confined to sandy hills overlying limestone. The compact bushes are not conspicuous until they flower in spring, when their silvery pink stands out in the veld.

Thamnochortus spicigerus, which grows in the same habitat, is one of the Cape reeds which was once extensively harvested for thatching roofs, but is little used nowadays.

Sundew *Drosera cistiflora*

The Malgas lily *Cybistetes longifolia*

The butterfly flower *Monsonia speciosa*

Like the renosterveld areas farther north, the Swartland of the South West region has been almost completely transformed by cultivation, mainly of wheat. There are, however, a number of public and private reserves where some of the especially beautiful plants of this veld type can be seen. Most of them are spring flowers but *Cybistetes longifolia*, the Malgas lily, like most Cape species of the Amaryllidaceae family, produces its uniquely lovely, densely packed and fragrant flowers in autumn.

Monsonia speciosa, one of the geranium family, Geraniaceae, is a soft, spring-flowering perennial whose flower petals have a distinctively characteristic texture.

Sundews, such as this *Drosera cistiflora*, are insectivorous: their leaves have long, very sticky hairs that trap small insects which are then digested by enzymes produced by the plants. In this way sundews can absorb nutrients like nitrogen and phosphorus, which are less easily available from the soils in which they grow. Sundews generally grow in seeps, where the soils are consequently extremely leached.

The wynkelkie *Geissorhiza radians*

Gazania krebsiana

Drosera cistiflora

Geissorhiza monanthos

The Darling area is famous for its spring flower displays. At this time, the veld, normally drab, is bright with colour; an extra joy is the individual beauty of many of the flowers which make up the display. Among these are the wynkelkie (*Geissorhiza radians*) and its relative *Geissorhiza monanthos*. It is in this area that the brilliant orange-red form of *Drosera cistiflora* grows. Daisies make a major contribution to the display, and none is more beautifully marked than the well known gazania, *Gazania krebsiana*.

Moraea aristata may once have been more widespread in the renosterveld areas which used to surround Table Mountain, but is now critically rare, clinging to survival in one conserved plot in the midst of Cape Town's congested suburbia.

Moraea aristata

Watsonia borbonica subsp. *borbonica*

Brachysiphon fucatus

Capetonians and visitors to the city are uniquely privileged to have one of the earth's great natural treasures literally within walking distance of the city centre. Much more than a world-renowned landmark, Table Mountain is home to a huge number of fynbos plant species, many of them endemic. On this massive and familiar pile of sandstone rock, and on the rest of the Peninsula mountain chain, can be found more plant species than grow in the whole of the British Isles. The waboom (*Protea nitida*) is generally found in fairly dry situations, including Table Mountain's steep, rocky front face that looks north over the city centre and Table Bay harbour. By contrast *Brachysiphon fucatus*, a Peninsula endemic, prefers a damper habitat such as the Saddle between the mountain and Devil's Peak. From here the distant Hottentots Holland mountains can be seen rising above an autumnal fog bank which screens the urban sprawl. *Brachysiphon fucatus* is one of the more showy members of the endemic fynbos family, the Penaeaceae. *Watsonia borbonica* subsp. *borbonica* is not confined to the Peninsula, and is particularly floriferous in the season following a fire.

< The waboom *Protea nitida*

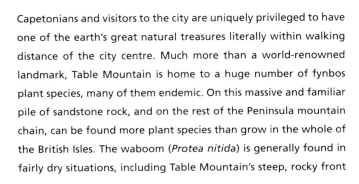

The blue disa *Herschelianthe graminifolia*

The red disa *Disa uniflora*

The red disa (*Disa uniflora*) and the blue disa (*Herschelianthe graminifolia*) are the best known of Table Mountain's many orchids. Both are late summer flowering. The blue disa grows on open slopes, but the red is found near streams or on seeps. *Disa uniflora* is one of the large number of orange or red summer or early autumn flowers that is pollinated by the Table Mountain pride butterfly (*Aeropetes tulbaghia*).

Erica coccinea is a very widespread species with many different forms; this one features among the host of *Erica* species found on the Cape Peninsula.

Erica coccinea

The Guernsey lily *Nerine sarniensis*

Lion's Head's granite lower slopes are home to one of the region's largest populations of the silver tree (*Leucadendron argenteum*). When part of the area recently burnt, the belladonna lily (*Amaryllis belladonna*), not seen here for many years, and the Guernsey lily (*Nerine sarniensis*) flowered in extravagant splendour a few weeks afterwards.

The belladonna lily *Amaryllis belladonna*

The silver tree *Leucadendron argenteum* (male)

Orphium frutescens

Pelargonium cucullatum

Dilatris pillansii

Orphium frutescens is seldom found far from the sea, generally growing in dense groups in marshy areas and flowering in summer. *Pelargonium cucullatum* is one of the Cape species of *Pelargonium* used to produce the range of cultivated 'geraniums' which brighten window boxes from Holland to Italy and farther afield. Like *Dilatris pillansii*, it is a fynbos species. *Dilatris pillansii* belongs to the small Haemadoraceae family, so named because its members exude a red sap when their underground parts are cut.

Gladiolus aureus

Leucadendron salignum

The monkey beetle *Trichostetha* sp. on *Leucospermum conocarpodendron* subsp. *viride*.

The Cape of Good Hope Nature Reserve is a very windy place, as the low, compact growth of this *Leucadendron salignum* bush testifies. Another notable member of the protea family, the tree pincushion (*Leucospermum conocarpodendron* subsp. *viride*) withstands the wind in a different way: it is a large, rigid shrub or small tree with stout branches and stem, and is common in the reserve and elsewhere on the Peninsula. In spring, these plants are favoured by orangebreasted sunbirds, which use them as perches and feed on the nectar and insects in the flowerheads.

The 'mountain dahlia' (*Liparia splendens*) carries large, nodding flowers which have a unique beauty and are also pollinated by sunbirds. *Gladiolus aureus* is an extremely rare Peninsula endemic.

The mountain dahlia *Liparia splendens*

The false heath *Audouinia capitata*

Stilbe ericoides

Staavia dodii

Hessea cinnamomea

In their frenetic dash to see Cape Point, few of the Cape of Good Hope Nature Reserve's annual half a million visitors bother to look at its treasure-house of fynbos plants. In summer, however, no one can overlook the brilliant white everlastings (*Syncarpha vestita*). The reserve contains many endemics, among them *Audouinia capitata*, the false heath, and *Staavia dodii*, both of which are members of the endemic fynbos family Bruniaceae. *Stilbe ericoides* belongs to another, the Stilbaceae. *Hessea cinnamomea* is a tiny amaryllid which is only ever seen flowering in the winter months immediately after a fire.

< The everlasting *Syncarpha vestita*

Elegia filacea

The Bainskloof and Du Toit's Kloof mountains form part of the huge mountain complex which is the core of the Cape Floral Kingdom. *Elegia filacea*, one of the Cape reeds which usually grows in dense colonies, flowers *en masse* in the Bainskloof mountains; *Leucospermum tottum* flowers on the steep slopes of Du Toit's Kloof in summer.

Leucospermum tottum >

The blushing bride *Serruria florida*

Serruria rosea

The queen protea *Protea magnifica*

The featherhead *Phylica pubescens*

The blushing bride, *Serruria florida*, and *Serruria rosea* are both rare endemics from the south-western Cape mountains. For many years, the blushing bride was thought to be extinct in nature, but its locality was rediscovered and it is now carefully conserved. These two species have been hybridized to produce a range of vigorous, free-flowering cultivars.

Protea magnifica, the queen protea, is a very widespread species with many different forms distributed over most of the major mountain ranges of the Cape Floral Kingdom. This red-flowered form grows in the Franschhoek mountains.

Elegia capensis is one of the best known Cape reeds (Restionaceae). It is cultivated fairly widely; in nature it is normally found growing socially next to mountain streams. *Phylica pubescens* and its close relative *P. plumosa*, both commonly called featherhead, are the two most attractive species of *Phylica*. Both are cultivated for their showy flowerheads and hairy foliage. *Phylica* is a large Cape Flora genus in the Rhamnaceae family; most *Phylica* species are not especially attractive.

Elegia capensis

Aloe plicatilis

The waterfall gladiolus *Gladiolus cardinalis*

Aloes are generally associated with savannah and grassland vegetation, but the fynbos has its endemic species. One of them is *Aloe plicatilis*, which grows into a large shrub favouring dry scree slopes high up in the mountain areas. The waterfall gladiolus, *Gladiolus cardinalis*, as its name suggests, is found only in running water high in the mountains. There can be no more beautiful sight in the fynbos than a dense group of these plants, clustered around a mountain waterfall, in full summer flower.

Brunsvigia marginata is another extravagantly lovely fynbos flower. One of the Amaryllidaceae, it is nowhere common but flowers best after fire. Its brilliant orange flowers, like those of *Gladiolus cardinalis*, are pollinated by the Table Mountain pride butterfly (*Aeropetes tulbaghia*). Superficially similar in shape and colour to the common form of the Guernsey lily (*Nerine sarniensis*) it is not as widely cultivated, even though the individual flowers are larger and carried more densely in the head.

Brunsvigia marginata >

Mimetes argenteus

The king protea *Protea cynaroides*

The Hottentots Holland mountains are considered to be the heart of the Cape fynbos, sustaining a profusion of rare and lovely plants. One of the rarest of these is *Glischrocolla formosa*, a member of the endemic fynbos family Penaeaceae. *Protea stokoei* grows only in these mountains; *Mimetes argenteus*, one of the silver mimetes, is more widespread. *Protea cynaroides*, the king protea, is even more so but this form is found only in this mountainous area.

Glischrocolla formosa

Protea stokoei

The marsh rose *Orothamnus zeyheri*

Orothamnus zeyheri, the marsh rose, is the only species in its genus. This lovely member of the protea family was once plentiful enough (though never common) to appear, occasionally, on the flower-sellers' stalls in Cape Town's Adderley Street. Conservationists thought that more careful protection of its mountain habitat against flower picking and fires would ensure its survival. Inexplicably, however, once thriving, healthy populations of the marsh rose began to dwindle. It was only after an uncontrolled fire burnt one of its locations and, soon after, a dense stand of seedlings sprouted, that the essential role of fire in the life-cycle of this and other fynbos plants began to be understood. Relatively short-lived, woody plants like the marsh rose and, in particular, *Mimetes hottentoticus*, another of the silver mimetes, need fairly frequent burning (every 10 to 15 years) so new generations can be produced from seed which cannot otherwise germinate. Older plants become unproductive and die off.

Mimetes hottentoticus

Erica patersonia

Elegia persistens

Erica patersonia and *E. campanularis* are two of the many erica species found in the Hottentots Holland mountains. The latter occurs in damp areas next to mountain streams whereas *E. patersonia* grows on seasonally wet flats below the mountains near Betty's Bay. *Elegia persistens* flowers in midsummer high in the mountains. The quintessential fynbos scene must be the mass flowering of leucadendrons, which

Erica campanularis

Witsenia maura

turns whole mountainsides yellow. Here, *Leucadendron microcephalum* colours the slopes of the Groenlandberg mountains. *Witsenia maura* is one of the woody Iridaceae, a group of plants restricted to the Cape fynbos and thought to be immensely ancient.

Nebelia sphaerocephala belongs to the Bruniaceae, one of seven endemic Cape Flora families.

Nebelia sphaerocephala

Leucadendron microcephalum

Bryomorphe lycopodioides

Phaenocoma prolifera

Roridula gorgonias

Lonchostoma monogynum

Ischyrolepis subverticillata (male)

Bryomorphe lycopodioides is one of the smallest of several fynbos species of daisy which grow as compact cushions on exposed sandstone rocks. *Phaenocoma prolifera,* an 'everlasting' daisy, is common on coastal mountain slopes, where it flowers in summer. *Lonchostoma monogynum* belongs to the Bruniaceae. *Roridula gorgonias* looks superficially like some of the sundews (*Drosera* sp.), but it and its sister *R. dentata* are, in fact, the only two species in another endemic fynbos family, the Roridulaceae. *Ischyrolepis subverticillata* is another large and attractive Cape reed.

Nivenia stokoei

Nivenia stokoei grows in the southern Hottentots Holland mountains. The genus *Nivenia* is the largest of the woody Iridaceae's three genera, and each of its ten species has intensely blue flowers. *Pillansia templemanii* is the only species in another fynbos genus of the Iridaceae. Confined to the same area, this plant flowers spectacularly during the season after a fire.

Pillansia templemanii and *Watsonia borbonica* subsp. *borbonica* >

Erica massonii

Retzia capensis is the only member of the endemic fynbos family Retziaceae. *Brunia stokoei* grows only in a limited area near the Palmiet River mouth. In summer the intense red flowers of *Crassula coccinea* stand out from the sandstone rocks among which it grows. *Erica massonii* produces its sticky flowers in the same season.

Crassula coccinea

Brunia stokoei

< *Retzia capensis*

The waterlily *Nymphaea nouchali* var. *caerulea*

Aristea biflora

The southern renosterveld areas, like the equivalent western ones, have also been extensively cultivated. Here, in remnant patches of renosterveld, grow some critically rare and lovely plants. One of these is *Moraea insolens*, whose flower's shape and colour are unusual for a moraea. (This species also has a creamy-yellow flowered form.) Another is *Aristea biflora*, which is seldom seen in flower except in the season after a fire. Both these treasures flower in springtime. The attractive waterlily, *Nymphaea nouchali* var. *caerulea* is anything but rare: common in standing water throughout the Cape Floral Kingdom (throughout Africa, in fact), it is a lovely sight in flower.

Moraea insolens

Erica longifolia

The Kleinrivier mountains run eastwards from near Hermanus into the mountains above Bredasdorp. This low range has its own share of endemics, among them the very rare *Erica bodkinii*, which has large, pendulous, waxy white flowers. *Brachysiphon acutus*, another endemic, belongs to the fynbos family Penaeaceae. It is pollinated by long-tongued flies (not the one shown here). *Erica bruniades* is widely distributed in the South West region, growing on damp, flat, sandy areas in the mountains. *Erica longifolia* has a similar distribution and occurs in a number of colour forms – yellow, pink, wine-red and white – in different localities. This form comes from the mountains above Napier, west of Bredasdorp.

Brachysiphon acutus

Erica bruniades

Erica bodkinii

Gladiolus carmineus

Roella rhodantha

The Caledon bluebell (*Gladiolus bullatus*) belongs to a group of related species which also includes *G. rogersii* and *G. inflatus*. This species grows in fynbos on the Caledon Swartberg, and also on the Table Mountain sandstone hills farther to the south-east. *Gladiolus carmineus* occurs in the same type of soil and is found along the coast where sandstone rocks meet the sea.

Potberg is an isolated Table Mountain sandstone ridge on the Agulhas Plain just west of the Breede River mouth. Because of its isolation, it has a number of endemic species, among them *Roella rhodantha*. The majority of fynbos *Roella* species, members of the Campanulaceae, have blue flowers but *Roella rhodantha* differs in having only pink and red forms, both found only on Potberg.

The Caledon bluebell *Gladiolus bullatus*

Othonna quinquedentata, on the south slopes of the Riviersonderend range.

Edmondia fasciculata and *Erica vestita*

Starting just east of Villiersdorp, the Riviersonderend range of mountains runs due east, ending just east of the town that gives the range its name. This is a rugged stretch of upland terrain with some high peaks. The south slopes are, typically, wetter than the north, and harbour patches of forest. *Othonna quinquedentata* is one of the daisy family with exaggeratedly long flowerstems, typically seen in profusion two to four years after fire and thereafter gradually outcompeted by slower growing plants. *Edmondia fasciculata* is another member of the same family – one of the everlastings – seen here on the north slopes of Jonaskop, one of the range's highest peaks. This form of *Protea cynaroides* grows on the steep south slopes of the Riviersonderend mountains.

The king protea *Protea cynaroides*

Tritoniopsis burchellii

Leucadendron burchellii (female)

The Riviersonderend mountains have their share of endemic species. One of the showiest of these is *Endonema retzioides*, a rare member of the Penaeaceae, which grows on well-watered southern slopes in the vicinity of the town of Riviersonderend. It is one of only two species in the genus *Endonema*; the other, *E. lateriflora*, is not especially attractive. *Leucadendron burchellii* is confined to a small area of this range, on the northern slopes of Jonaskop, one of its highest peaks. It flowers in early spring. *Tritoniopsis burchellii*, another plant honouring the noted 19th-century plant collector William Burchell, also grows on these slopes. It is another late summer-flowering plant which is pollinated by the Table Mountain pride butterfly (*Aeropetes tulbaghia*).

Endonema retzioides >

THE AGULHAS PLAIN

Unlike others of the Cape Floral Kingdom's six regions, most of the rocks and soils of the Agulhas Plain are, in pedological terms, of recent origin. The whole of this area has been below the sea at times in the past few million years, and the limestone hills and dunefields which line the coast are a result of the inundations. The large numbers of endemic plant species found here appeared when forms from inland areas conquered land previously submerged, and adapted to the new habitats provided by the region's varied rock and soil types. Because it is flat and fairly close to Cape Town, large expanses have been transformed by agriculture, but there are substantial tracts of natural vegetation both outside and inside protected areas such as the De Hoop Nature Reserve. There are moves to incorporate some of the remaining tracts of natural veld, situated outside the existing reserves, into a national park.

Anemone tenuifolia is the only anemone in the Cape Flora. It is closely related to the northern hemisphere anemones which have provided the well known garden plants. The species is widespread in the Cape Floral Kingdom, this particularly lovely form growing on the limestone hills of the coast near Bredasdorp. *Senecio elegans* is a common plant on the dunes, where it is a spectacular sight when it flowers *en masse*.

Anemone tenuifolia

Senecio elegans

Erica cerinthoides and the long-horned grasshopper.

Erica calcareophila

Lobostemon bellidiformis is a very rare plant which was only recently discovered. It grows to a large bush which, with its pale to dark pink tubular flowers reminiscent of the rhododendron's, looks somewhat out of place in the fynbos. *Erica cerinthoides* is common and, in fact, occurs all the way from the Cape to the mountains of KwaZulu-Natal, Mpumalanga and Swaziland. *Erica calcareophila*, on the other hand, is a rare local endemic from the limestone hills south of Bredasdorp.

Lobostemon bellidiformis

Delosperma sp.

The main centre of the mesembs (species of the family Mesembryanthemaceae) is the succulent Karoo vegetation of Namaqualand, but the Cape Flora contains a great many members, including this species of *Delosperma*, whose precise taxonomic status has not yet been resolved. The 'everlasting' daisies of the fynbos do indeed leave a lasting impression. *Edmondia sesamoides* is found in acid sandy soils, whereas *Syncarpha argyropsis* grows on limestone.

Syncarpha argyropsis

Edmondia sesamoides

Helichrysum chlorochrysum

Lachnaea aurea

Helichrysum chlorochrysum is an everlasting which grows in deep coastal sands. The orchid, *Herschelianthe lugens*, occurs on the seasonally inundated flats south of Bredasdorp. Most species of *Euchaetis* (in the Rutaceae family) have tiny, inconspicuous flowers but those of this particular one, *E. longibracteata*, are the exception. It is an endemic of the coastal limestone hills. *Lachnaea aurea* looks superficially just like a daisy but belongs, in fact, to the Thymelaeaceae. It grows in the fynbos of this region, where it is endemic.

Herschelianthe lugens

Euchaetis longibracteata

THE LANGEBERG RANGE

It may seem strange that a single mountain range characterizes one of the Cape Floral Kingdom's regions, but the sheer number of endemic species found on its slopes justifies the status. The Langeberg mountains run from near Montagu in the west, roughly parallel to the coast eastwards, to the Robinson Pass. Essentially the same Table Mountain sandstone rock formation continues eastwards as the Outeniqua and Tsitsikamma mountains. The southern forelands have been extensively modified by agriculture, but much of the mountain range remains pristine. The Grootvadersbos Wilderness Area is one of the places where visitors can see some of the region's special plants in their very beautiful natural setting. It is along this range and over the land towards the sea that the winter rainfall pattern of the western Cape changes to the all-year round rainfall of the southern Cape.

In spring dense stands of *Erica melanthera* bring a deep pink colour to huge swathes of the southern slopes of the mountains.

Pelargonium tricolor has a number of different colour morphs. This one, found on the dry northern foothills of the Langeberg range, is among the prettiest.

Pelargonium tricolor

Erica melanthera

Leucadendron tradouwense (female)

The protea family (Proteaceae) includes several of the Langeberg region's many endemic plants. The small pincushion *Leucospermum mundii* is one of these. There are forms with velvety leaves and others with smooth ones, but the flower-heads of this elegant little plant are unmistakable. It grows on the fairly dry, lower mountain slopes.

Leucadendron tradouwense is another rare local endemic. Its species name derives from its locality – near the magni-ficently scenic Tradouw Pass which cuts through the Langeberg range between Swellendam and Heidelberg.

Leucospermum mundii

Leucadendron radiatum (male)

Mimetes splendidus is another of the silver mimetes. This spectacular plant is not a Langeberg region endemic – it is also found on the Outeniqua and Tsitsikamma mountains – but is never common. Populations occur sporadically on the high, wet southern slopes of these ranges.

Leucadendron radiatum is a narrow endemic of the region, confined to the tops of several neighbouring peaks, and is rare. The plant is thought to be a palaeoendemic – a form from ancient times, clinging precariously to life in its last refuge, high in the mountains, where the climate is sympathetic.

Mimetes splendidus

Erica barrydalensis

Erica barrydalensis, *E. blenna* (the Riversdale heath) and *Geissoloma marginata* are all Langeberg endemics. *Geissoloma* is the sole member of one of the Cape Flora's endemic families, the Geissolomaceae. *Erica blenna* comes from the southern slopes of the range; *Erica barrydalensis*, from the very arid, northern slopes fringing the Little Karoo. *Gladiolus rogersii*, the Riversdale bluebell, is more widespread. This form comes from the mountains west of the Robinson Pass.

Geissoloma marginata

The Riversdale heath *Erica blenna*
The Riversdale bluebell *Gladiolus rogersii* >

THE SOUTH INLAND MOUNTAINS

The dramatic range of mountains called the Swartberg, which separates the Cape Floral Kingdom from the Great Karoo, contains some of the Cape's highest places. This is a place of harsh contrasts – in winter the high ground is frozen solid for weeks on end, in summer the rocks bake. While the peaks and southern slopes receive moderate rain, the northern ones are dry. Snow often falls in winter. The mountains' plant life reflects this environment, the high peaks carrying a low-growing cover of plants specially adapted to the rigorous conditions. To the south lies the Little Karoo, an arid valley in the rain shadow of the Outeniqua mountains, where succulent Karoo vegetation, closely allied to the plant life of Namaqualand, can be seen. Spread along the length of the Little Karoo is a broken range of dry mountains that includes Touwsberg, Gamkaberg, Rooiberg and the Kammanassies.

Brachysiphon microphyllus was discovered only recently. This small member of the Penaeaceae grows in the crevices of Table Mountain sandstone rocks high on Touwsberg, and on the neighbouring Klein Swartberg range.

Leucadendron comosum subsp. *comosum* occurs on the Rooiberg and the Swartberg mountains. The woody cones produced by female plants are among the largest in the genus.

Brachysiphon microphyllus

Leucadendron comosum subsp. *comosum* (male)

Mimetes chrysanthus

Hypocalyptus sophoroides

Leucadendron singulare (male)

Leucadendron pubibracteolatum (female)

Mimetes chrysanthus was one of the botanical finds of the century: its discovery in 1987 by Willie Julies, a game guard in the Gamka Mountain Nature Reserve, caused a minor sensation. This is neither a tiny plant (it is a bush that grows to over 2 metres high) nor an inconspicuous one – its brilliant yellow flowerheads stand out in the veld – so it is extraordinary that it remained unknown after centuries of botanical exploration in the Cape Floral Kingdom. Recently, the species was also found on the dry northern foothills of the Outeniquas. *Leucadendron singulare* is a rare species from high in the Kammanassie mountains. *L. pubibracteolatum* also grows there and on neighbouring ranges on both sides of the Little Karoo. *Hypocalyptus sophoroides* is a tall legume which generally prefers stream-side sites, but is also found on the top of Gamka mountain.

Erica discolor flowers in summer on the dry northern slopes of the mountains of the Little Karoo and the Swartberg.

Erica discolor

Schotia afra

The Little Karoo is the dry valley between the Swartberg mountains and the Langeberg and Outeniqua ranges. Because of the aridity and predominantly Bokkeveld shale soils, the vegetation here is quite distinct from that of the adjoining mountains.

Nymania capensis (the klapperbos) is known more for its bright pink or red seed capsules than its insignificant flowers, and is a familiar sight in the Little Karoo. *Schotia afra*, a legume (Fabaceae), grows in seasonal stream-beds, where it carries its deep red flowers in summer.

< The klapperbos *Nymania capensis*

The spekboom *Portulacaria afra*

The wild pomegranate *Rhigozum obovatum*

The summer-flowering *Acacia karroo* is common in the dry parts of the Cape Floral Kingdom. The spekboom (*Portulacaria afra*) and the wild pomegranate (*Rhigozum obovatum*) grow on dry shale slopes and tend to flower opportunistically following good rains. *Euphorbia atrispina* is an example of the typically succulent plant life of the Little Karoo.

Locust on *Euphorbia atrispina*.

Sweetthorn *Acacia karroo*

Nivenia binata

Nivenia binata is another member of the woody Iridaceae group of plants, and one of three *Nivenia* species on the Swartberg range. *N. stenosiphon* is found at the western end of the Klein Swartberg (and in the neighbouring Touwsberg), *N. parviflora* farther east on the same range. *N. binata* grows in the Swartberg Pass area where it is a conspicuous and lovely sight in late spring. Flowering at the same time and in the same area is the very rare and localised *Stirtonanthus taylorianus*, one of the legumes.

The daisy *Berkheya francisci,* with its distinctive, spiny leaves, flowers high in the Swartberg in summer.

< *Berkheya francisci*

Stirtonanthus taylorianus

Members of the protea family (Proteaceae) form a large and conspicuous part of the shrubby vegetation of the Swartberg range. Many of them are striking plants, none more lovely than two *Protea* species typical of the range. *P. venusta* has a wide distribution which also includes the Kammanassie mountains and forms a dense, sprawling bush which trails over the rocks in high and sheltered places. *P. aristata* was once thought to be very rare but is now known from several localities in the Klein Swartberg mountains above Ladismith.

Protea venusta

Protea aristata

Leucadendron dregei (female)

Leucadendron tinctum is one of the Cape Flora's plants which has a very wide distribution. In this region it grows on the Rooiberg in the Little Karoo, and on the Swartberg range. In bud, here, the involucral leaves are a delicate plum colour, which turns to creamy yellow when the plant is in full flower.

Leucadendron album grows in large stands that are particularly conspicuous when the light reflects off its silvery leaves. *L. dregei* is a plant from the high peaks, where it sprawls over rocks.

Struthiola eckloniana belongs to the Thymelaeaceae family. This deep-bronze flowered form grows alongside the road between Die Hel and the top of the Swartberg Pass.

Struthiola eckloniana

< *Leucadendron tinctum* (male in bud)

Leucadendron album (male)

THE SOUTH EAST

*T*he last of the Cape Floral Kingdom's six regions, the South East, includes the Outeniqua/Tsitsikamma range and its coastal plateau together with the mountains near Port Elizabeth. Inland, the Baviaanskloof is contained by the Kouga and Baviaanskloofberg ranges. Although fynbos is the characteristic vegetation of the mountains and the coastal plateau, it becomes more grassy in the east, a consequence of its contact with the savannah and grassland vegetation types of the eastern Cape. The Baviaanskloof contains large areas of valley bushveld, a tall thicket vegetation type which is also characteristic of the eastern Cape. One of the glories of this region is the temperate forest which graces the southern slopes of the Outeniqua and Tsitsikamma mountains and the coastal plateau. Because of these different plant communities, the flora of this region is varied.

The Garden Route coast is the loveliest in the Cape Floral Kingdom. Despite the encroachment of farmlands, excessive afforestation, heavy infestation by alien trees and, especially in the last ten years, of aggressive and ill-planned commercial 'development' over large parts, there are some stretches little affected by man. One of these is the Tsitsikamma National Park, where you can see one of the Cape Flora's hibiscuses, *Hibiscus trionum*.

Hibiscus trionum

Gazania rigens on the coastal rocks at Storms River mouth.

Gladiolus carinatus

Anisodontea scabrosa

Another plant in the Malvaceae family is *Anisodontea scabrosa*, a species whose leaves are covered in rough hairs and which bears typically hibiscus-looking flowers that range in colour from light to dark pink. The species grows in a variety of habitats ranging from forest edges to open scrub veld along the coast. It can flower at any time of the year.

The scented flowers of *Freesia alba* are produced in spring. This plant is found on two other unspoilt, conserved parts of the coast – in the Goukamma Nature Reserve and on the Robberg peninsula near Plettenberg Bay. The Goukamma contains what are said to be the highest vegetated dunes in South Africa. This form of *Gladiolus carinatus* grows in the dune fynbos, flowering in spring.

< *Freesia alba*

Dietes iridioides

Burchellia bubalina, one of several wholly unrelated plants with the common name wild pomegranate, is a shrub or small tree found in both scrub forest and high forest. *Dietes iridioides* is often seen along forest paths and on the edge of clearings. Its small flowers are produced mainly in spring and early summer. Arum lilies (*Zantedeschia aethiopica*) are found all over the Cape Floral Kingdom. These particular plants were in deep forest, growing next to a pool with black peaty water.

The arum lily *Zantedeschia aethiopica*

The wild pomegranate *Burchellia bubalina*

The Outeniqua yellowwood *Podocarpus falcatus*

The Cape chestnut *Calodendrum capense*

Plectranthus fruticosus

Although the southern Cape's forests are not especially interesting to the botanist – they contain very few species of plants compared with the surrounding fynbos vegetation and, for that matter, with forests farther north in southern Africa – they do provide a uniquely lovely environment. There are two species of yellow-woods found here; by far the more easily recognised is the renowned Outeniqua yellowwood, *Podocarpus (Afrocarpus) falcatus*. The older trees are the great giants of the forests, towering over the canopy and characteristically festooned with old man's beard lichen (*Usnia* sp.). The Cape chestnut (*Calodendrum capense*) is a glorious sight when it flowers in midsummer. Trees in full, silvery-pink bloom stand out on the forested hillsides, prominent against the muted green of the other trees. This species belongs to the same family (Rutaceae) as the buchus (*Agathosma* spp.) of the fynbos, and as citrus. *Plectranthus fruticosus* is a soft-leafed herb which grows in deep shade on the forest floor. Its delicate flowers, ranging in colour from pale to dark mauve, are produced mainly in the summer months.

< Forest stream with tree ferns.

Gladiolus sempervirens

Ceratandra grandiflora

Mountain fynbos in the South East region covers not only the slopes of the mountains but also the coastal plateaux, which are where some of the typically very tall, dense fynbos of the southern Cape can be seen. There is a prime stand of this type of vegetation at the western end of the Tsitsikamma National Park's De Vasselot section. One of the Cape Flora's red hot pokers, *Kniphofia uvaria*, and one of this area's most striking orchids, *Ceratandra grandiflora*, flower here in summer.

Gladiolus sempervirens, by contrast, grows in sheltered spots high in the Outeniqua and Tsitsikamma mountains, sometimes on forest margins. Its large, brilliant red blooms, produced in the late summer, form part of the guild of red and orange flowers pollinated by the Table Mountain pride butterfly (*Aeropetes tulbaghia*). This plant is one of a group of large red-flowered gladioli which include *Gladiolus cardinalis* and *G. stefaniae* as well as some Drakensberg and eastern Cape species.

The red hot poker *Kniphofia uvaria* >

The George (or Knysna) lily *Cyrtanthus elatus*

Mimetes pauciflorus

The George (or Knysna) lily, *Cyrtanthus elatus*, is one of the Cape Flora's best known amaryllids, cultivated widely for its large, extravagantly lovely flowers. These are generally a deep orange-red in colour but pink and even white forms occur naturally. The George lily grows in a variety of habitats ranging from cliffs just above the sea to high, open mountain slopes and even in forest clearings, but always in places where there is a steady supply of water. The species flowers profusely after a mountain fire.

Mimetes pauciflorus, one of the protea family, is restricted to the wet southern slopes of the Outeniqua and Tsitsikamma ranges. It flowers in late spring and early summer, when the bright yellow flowerheads stand out against the surrounding fynbos.

The strawberry everlasting *Syncarpha eximia*

Leucospermum glabrum

The wet southern mountain slopes are also the preferred habitat of one of the region's endemic pincushions, *Leucospermum glabrum*. This plant has a very closely related sister species, *L. pluridens,* which grows on the very dry northern slopes of the Outeniqua mountains, on the edge of the Little Karoo. The two species evidently evolved from a common ancestor, the one adapting to an arid environment, the other to a moist one. Now separated by a physical barrier, the two populations are distinct.

The strawberry everlasting, *Syncarpha eximia*, which belongs to the daisy family, is a plant with an unusual growth habit: the plants, which are seldom branched, grow nearly 2 metres tall. Softly-haired grey leaves cover the stems, at the ends of which are the densely packed, brightly coloured flowers.

Erica densifolia is one of several southern Cape species which have red flowers with green tips. The flowers are very sticky, and are produced abundantly in summer.

Erica densifolia

Plumbago auriculata

The kreupelboom *Oldenburgia grandis*

It is difficult to delineate a hard-and-fast eastern boundary to the Cape Floral Kingdom. Valley bushveld, a vegetation type characteristic of the eastern Cape, reaches into the Baviaanskloof and occurs in patches along the coast. *Plumbago auriculata*, the plumbago grown in gardens all over the world, is a prominent part of this vegetation. *Oldenburgia grandis* – known as the kreupelboom – is one of the large, woody plants in the daisy family and typically grows in the grassy fynbos found on the mountains north of Port Elizabeth (within the Cape Floral Kingdom's boundaries), but also on the Suurberg just outside.

Cyrtanthus flammosus is another plant only recently discovered. As far as is known it is a narrow endemic, from the Baviaanskloof, which flowers in summer. Its brilliant orange-red colour is typical of other related *Cyrtanthus* species with large open flowers, plants such as the George lily and the Kei lily (*C. elatus* and *C. sanguineus*).

Cyrtanthus flammosus >

THE CAPE FLORA

ORIGINS

Because the human life-span is so short, we tend to regard the natural world (apart from its seasonal rhythms) as fixed and unchanging. It isn't. The earth's surface, the atmosphere and all the living things that occupy land, sea and sky are continually changing, mostly over unimaginably long periods. We know that the earth is some 5 000 million years old, recorded human history only a few thousand. To understand how the Cape Flora came to be, it is first necessary to stretch our perception of time a millionfold to comprehend the rate of geological processes.

If you were to realize one of humankind's favourite fantasies and travel back some 4 000 million years, you would see an unrecognisable landscape, something more like the moon's surface, a world devoid of life. Change direction, move forward 1 000 or 2 000 million years, and you would alight on a planet on which the first, incredibly primitive, life forms were beginning to appear.

Sandstone strata above the Swartberg Pass.

About 1 000 million years ago, what is now the Cape was part of the huge southern supercontinent known as Gondwana, which included areas that later became separate land masses – Africa, Antarctica, Australia, New Zealand, South America, India and Madagascar. The present-day Cape lay submerged near the shores of a vast inland lake. Over the next 300 odd million years, soil eroded from around its shore to settle on the bottom of the lake and became compacted to form rock. About 550 million years ago, these sedimentary rocks were buckled and folded by the cracking and movement of the earth's crust which, in places, allowed molten magma from the planetary core to reach the surface. Some of these ancient rocks can be seen today, among them the Malmesbury shales of the Swartland north of Cape Town, one of South Africa's major wheat growing areas; the limestone that contains the well-known Cango Caves, north of Oudtshoorn; and the granite domes – solidified magma – which are a characteristic feature of Cape Town's Atlantic seaboard, of the Paarl area and of the Cape west coast.

The mountains which emerged from these ancient folding processes were subsequently worn down over the aeons by erosion to form an essentially level plain. This was the site for a second period of inundation and sedimentation, lasting from 450 to 300 million years ago, that formed the rocks making up most of the south-western and southern Cape's surface today. First came the Table Mountain group, made up mainly of sandstones laid down in a layer up to 3 000 metres thick, then the Bokkeveld shales, followed finally by the Witteberg series of quartzites. In contrast with the ancient sediments and the newer Bokkeveld shales, the sandstones and quartzites are very deficient in elements such as nitrogen, phosphorus, potassium and magnesium, all of which are the essential ingredients for plant growth.

The first primitive land plants appeared on earth during this period. So did the world's first insects and amphibians.

Over a period of 65 million years, from about 280 million years ago, the Gondwanan surface was shattered by volcanic activity, the first sign that the supercontinent was breaking up. In the south, the gigantic forces that were unleashed pleated parts of its surface, which then broke in places, pushing up huge slabs of sedimentary rock to stand with their strata tilted, sometimes vertical, many thousands of metres above the surrounding land. This folding and shearing ran parallel with the lines along which Gondwana was, here, later to fragment. In what was to become the Cape, these lines ran roughly north-south in the west, and east-west in the south. The so-called fold mountains formed in this way are the ones we see today, though then they stood several times higher. From

Leucadendron salignum

that time to the present, the forces of erosion have worn them down to a fraction of their original height, in the process washing the softer, more easily eroded shales into the valleys and leaving the harder quartzites and sandstones exposed on the mountain tops and higher slopes, their tilted strata dramatically obvious in many places.

This cataclysmic period saw the appearance on earth of the first cone-bearing plants, the gymnosperms (about 230 million years ago), and the first reptiles (250 million years ago).

When Gondwana started to fragment about 140 million years ago, the ancient area of the Cape was covered with conifer-like gymnosperm forests with an understorey of ferns. The first flowering plants, angiosperms, appeared here well after Antarctica and Australia had broken away from Africa; southern South America finally separated from Africa somewhat later, leaving the Cape coast much as it is now. By the time another 25 million years had passed, flowering plants dominated the African landscape. At the time when the dinosaurs suddenly became extinct, 65 million years ago, the Cape – like the rest of Africa and the other Gondwanan fragments – was

Previous pages A colourful profusion of *Watsonia zeyheri* after a fire near Betty's Bay.

Erica tumida

covered with tropical rainforest which, in the Cape region, contained yellowwood trees (*Podocarpus* spp.), relics of the ancient conifer forests, similar to the giant yellowwoods (*Podocarpus falcatus*) of the Knysna forests, as well as the ancestors of trees now found only in Africa's tropical forests or on the other continents. In the Cape of that distant time there were also members of the Proteaceae and Restionaceae, families which are today so characteristic of fynbos. Throughout Africa the vegetation varied very little from one region to another. Not long after the disappearance of the great dinosaurs, Antarctica broke away from Australia.

The next 60 million years were marked by little geological activity at the Cape but by huge upheavals farther north in Africa, which gave birth to the East and Central African mountains and the Great Rift Valley. Mammals now dominated the African landscape. During the same period, the earth's poles cooled so that the climate of the Cape and of North Africa became very different from that in the equatorial regions of the continent. As a result, the Cape and high mountain regions of Central and East Africa developed a temperate climate drier than that of their surroundings. The ancestors of the Cape fynbos, and of the fynbos vegetation found now in places elsewhere on the continent, began to evolve on these temperate 'islands' while tropical forest covered the rest of Africa. Then, about 35 million years ago, Africa's climate became drier; the ancient fynbos patches in the Cape and on the temperate islands to the north expanded as the forests, faced with less favourable conditions, receded. Later, as the climate became more humid again, the forest regained some of the ground formerly lost to the ancient fynbos, pushing it back to sites where the soil was too poor or too thin to support tropical forest. In the process, new fynbos forms evolved and some old forms became extinct. New forms were also added to the fynbos plants with Gondwanan ancestry as plants from the then northern hemisphere families, such as the Rosaceae and Ericaceae, 'island-hopped' down Africa to the Cape.

About 20 million years ago, a cold-water current began to circulate Antarctica, now a completely separate Gondwanan fragment. The earth's poles became colder and the southern continent froze over. Sea levels began to drop, leaving sand exposed around the Cape coast, loose surface material which was blown inland to form sand plains and dune fields. Periodic warmer episodes flooded coastal areas and marine sediments were deposited, later to become the limestone hills today found along the Cape coast. Some 10 million years later, as temperatures throughout the world continued to drop, and the Antarctic ice-sheet expanded, ocean currents began to influence the climate at the southern tip of Africa. The establishment of the cold Benguela stream off the Cape west coast caused aridification so that the ancient tropical forests, which had been the dominant vegetation for so long, gave way to temperate forests and grasslands still interspersed with patches of fynbos. Recurrent fires became a feature of the environment. Moreover, for the first time, as the South Atlantic high pressure cell became established about 3 million years ago, the southern tip of Africa experienced a summer dry-winter wet rainfall pattern. In addition, the region was becoming even drier, so that the temperate forests and grasslands increasingly gave way to the fynbos which, up to then, had been restricted to inhospitable sites, and which had developed hard leaves and other adaptive strategies to cope with harsh conditions. In the process, some new habitats became available and other fynbos forms evolved.

As fynbos took over from grasslands and forests, neither of which could withstand the frequent fires and increasingly dry summers, the southern part of the Cape (defined

Protea odorata

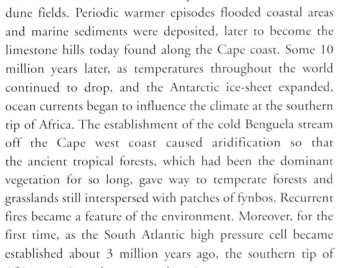

Protea mucronifolia

by the western and southern mountain ranges) became partially isolated. Semi-desert conditions had developed to the north, effectively cutting off what is now the Cape Floral region from the grasslands and savannah which were appearing even farther north. Only in the east was contact maintained with the evolving savannah and the grasslands. Temperate forest survived in the Cape, where conditions were still favourable enough, but by 3 million years ago fynbos had become the dominant vegetation of the region and the stage was set for the appearance of what we know as the Cape Flora.

The past 2 million years on earth have been dominated by long periods of intense cold broken every 100 millennia or so by relatively short warmer periods. This is the time when the Cape flora underwent an extraordinary diversification.

During the long glacial periods, the polar ice sheets expanded – though with different consequences in the northern and southern hemispheres. At times the Arctic ice-cap covered most of the North American and Eurasian land masses, but the southern tip of Africa lay too far north. The polar caps contained gigantic quantities of water, so sea levels dropped during the glacial periods to rise again during the short, warm interglacial periods (we are now approaching the end of one of these). Drops in the ocean levels exposed large areas of the southern and south-western Cape (which had been inundated again during the interglacials), and, at times, the Agulhas Plain stretched 100 kilometres and more south of the Langeberg and Outeniqua mountains.

The rapid increase in the number of Cape Flora species over the past 3 million years or so is a consequence of a unique combination of environmental factors which, together, produced a multitude of changing habitats and microhabitats to which plants adapted by evolving new forms. The major factors in the process have been the low nutrient content of the quartzite- and sandstone-derived soils in comparison with shale and limestone soils; recurrent fires; the broken, rocky terrain of the mountain ranges; the great difference, at this latitude, between the amount of sunshine falling on north-facing slopes and that warming the south-facing ones; alternating dry and wet periods, and the directional patterns of rainfall and wind.

Low-lying land exposed during the interglacial periods was open to colonization by plants able to adapt to the new conditions. Inundations during the interglacials isolated previously more widespread forms. During this time, many closely related species, plants such as the renosterveld proteas, *Protea odorata* and *Protea mucronifolia*, made their appearance.

Throughout this period, the Cape Flora was largely isolated from the savannah, forest, and grassland vegetation – which covered most of Africa – by the arid areas of what we now call the Great Karoo, Namaqualand and the Namib desert. However, there was contact in the east – hence the remarkable mixture of vegetation types found there today. The eastern Cape is truly the meeting place of the Cape Flora and the vegetation of the rest of sub-Saharan Africa.

Why did the small patches of fynbos vegetation on the African mountains to the north not diversify to the same extent as the Cape Flora? Probably because the nutrient deficient soils of these uplands, on which the fynbos grows, are severely limited in extent, though there have been other major factors, among them the weather patterns and insolation (the amount of sunlight received). Very recently the relatively constant and moderate conditions, sustained over space and time, have favoured forest and grassland at the expense of fynbos (particularly grassland, whose expansion has accelerated since man started burning the veld annually to promote grazing for his animals). In tropical Africa fynbos was, and is, confined to marginal areas unsuitable for grass or trees.

The distribution patterns of the genera of major Cape plant families illustrate the

Mimetes stokoei

diversification that has taken place here. For example, the family Proteaceae (like the Bruniaceae, an ancient Gondwanan family), has representatives of only three of its African genera outside the Cape Floral Kingdom; all its other African genera are found only within the region. Most species of these three genera belong to the Cape Flora. Of the roughly 115 species of *Protea*, only about 40 are found in Africa outside the Cape Floral Kingdom; of the 49 species of *Leucospermum*, only four. Just three species of *Leucadendron* occur to the north. *Raspalia trigyna* is one of only two species of the Bruniaceae found outside the region. These distributions raise some intriguing questions: are these extra Cape Flora species relics of a time when the ancient fynbos was more uniform and widespread in Africa? Did families and genera now represented only in the region, or their ancestors, once occur elsewhere in Africa? We might never learn the answers.

What we do know is that extinction is as much a part of the development of any region's flora as is speciation. *Mimetes stokoei*, one of the silver mimetes, has disappeared, most likely as part of the natural process, over the past few decades. The Cape Flora does contain plants which systematists recognize as being very primitive and which are invariably highly localized, clinging to survival and eluding extinction in the only microhabitats, often high in the mountains, which can now support them. These refugees from bygone ages, periods when they were probably more widespread, are called palaeoendemics. *Klattia flava* is one such. Their presence emphasizes the extreme antiquity of much of the Cape Flora. In stark contrast, the flowers that grow over most of Europe, North America and continental Asia had to establish themselves after the glaciers and the Arctic ice-sheet last retreated, a matter of just 10 000 years or so ago. As a result, the northern biomes contain far fewer species, and these are generally widespread.

Klattia flava

INTERACTIONS

In their natural habitat, individual plants do not grow in isolation: they are in constant competition with other plants – for space (above and below ground), for light, and for water and nutrients from the soil, which they need to grow and flower. In addition, many species compete for the attention of insects, birds and animals whose help they need in pollinating their flowers or distributing their seed.

Plants must also survive the stresses and come to terms with the constraints imposed by the physical environment – the type and depth of the soil, the quality and quantity of sunshine, the incidence of rain and snow, the extremes of temperature, and wind. A population of a species growing healthily in its habitat is there because it has managed to adapt to the range of physical conditions it experiences through the seasons, because it is able to breed effectively, and because its individual plants can compete successfully with members of the other species.

The plants of the Cape Flora are as varied as the region's extraordinary range of micro-habitats. Soil type largely determines the type of vegetation cover; the shallow, sandy soils derived from the Table Mountain sandstone and Witteberg quartzite rocks, which predominate on the mountains, are so leached of nutrients, and therefore acidic, that the fynbos plants that grow naturally on them have evolved special and distinctive adaptations. Micro-organisms probably play a major role in the way nutrients are absorbed from these soils,

Snow on the Groenlandberg mountains.

although very little is known about this. Particularly remarkable are the plants adapted to living on the rocks themselves, their roots lodged in small crevices. These species not only have to withstand an extreme shortage of water and nutrients, but also wide temperature fluctuations without the insulating and shading benefits provided by neighbouring plants. However, they are highly successful species, having occupied an environmental niche in which competition from other growth is negligible. It is significant that such plants, called petrophiles, are confined exclusively to rocks. They cannot compete in what would appear to be a less stressful environment – the soil next to the rocks.

Anyone who walks the Cape mountains soon sees that the fynbos vegetation cover changes with an increase in altitude

Frontal rain on Jonaskop in the Riviersonderend mountains.

Wind in the Bainskloof mountains.

as well as with the attitude of the slope on which it grows. North-facing hillsides are always drier and carry a different set of plants from south slopes. Sheltered valleys will support a range of plants quite unlike those on exposed ridges. Likewise, the fynbos on mountain peaks which are regularly covered with snow for extended periods in winter is different from the fynbos below the snow-line. The vegetation cover high in the coastal mountains of the south-western Cape, which receive appreciable moisture in the rain-free summer months – from cloud formed from water vapour brought in from the sea by the prevailing south-easterly winds – differs completely from the vegetation of the inland mountain peaks. All these plant communities are in a finely tuned balance, and any long-term change in their environment will lead to a corresponding change in their species make-up.

Recurrent fires have been and are an integral part of the fynbos and renosterveld environments. All their species are specially adapted to fire, though there is wide variation within fynbos communities in the way individual species cope with the effect of burning. Some react very quickly to fire; many geophytes flower spectacularly but only during the following season and, for some – like the fire lily (*Cyrtanthus ventricosus*) and the rare *Haemanthus canaliculatus* – this is the only time they produce flowers. For many soft-leaved herbs, such as *Mairea coriacea*, the one or two years after a fire is the only time during which they can enjoy a trouble-free growth and flowering before the competition from other plant forms becomes too much for them. Some shrubs, like many *Aspalathus* species (members of the legume family), grow rapidly from seed to flower only two to four years after the burn before they are also overwhelmed, in the years that follow, by slower growing shrubs. Many fynbos plants have evolved rootstocks which manage to survive undamaged by fire and from which they can sprout new growth immediately after a conflagration.

Other plants, among them some of the *Leucadendron* and *Protea* species, store their seeds in woody cones, where they remain for years until a fire destroys the parent plant – and opens its cones to release the seeds into an environment optimal for their germination, so producing a new generation. This strategy, called serotiny, also minimizes the predation of the seeds by rodents.

Haemanthus canaliculatus flowering after fire.

Mairea coriacea

Aeropetes tulbaghia on *Nerine sarniensis.*   Monkey beetle *Pachycnema* sp. on *Ixia curta.*   Striped mouse on *Protea montana.*

As any flower photographer here will tell you, wind is not in short supply in the region. Many Cape Flora species rely on wind to transfer pollen from the flowers of one individual to another's to effect fertilization and, because this is a haphazard method, pollen is produced in great quantities. Other plants use the wind to distribute their seeds. Most species, however, employ more accurate mobile agents to transfer pollen from flower to flower. Plants growing naturally do not produce showy flowers simply to delight humans – they expend the huge amounts of energy required

Greater double collared sunbird taking nectar from *Aloe arborescens.*

in their production only to attract pollinators. Many of the Cape's flowers are fertilized by generalist pollinators such as honey bees (*Apis mellifera*) and a huge variety of insects, including butterflies and beetles. Prominent among these are protea scarab beetles and a range of monkey beetles. The latter use flowers not only as food sources but also as mating sites; close examination of many spring-flowering species will reveal the insect equivalent of a Roman orgy. Moreover, the petals of these flowers often have markings that mimic the appearance of female monkey beetles, an ingenious ploy designed by selection to attract love-lorn males.

Other plants have evolved flowers which are attractive to specific pollinators. Several species of *Gladiolus*, for example, are scented only after dark in order to lure night-flying moths. Some orchids and diascias produce an oil in their flowers that is sought after by certain species of bee: in reaching for the oil, the bee transfers pollen from one flower to another. Some *Protea* and *Leucospermum* species produce flowerheads with a yeasty smell and positioned close to the ground. These are visited at night by mice, which feed on the nectar but also collect a substantial quantity of pollen on their fur, and this is carried to other flowerheads.

One of the more bizarre pollination strategies involves the flowers of *Orphium frutescens*. These are are buzz-pollinated: pollen is not exposed but contained instead in tubular shaped anthers with a pore at the end, and is released only when the anthers are vibrated at a very specific frequency. This buzzing is provided by carpenter bees, which crouch over the anthers and vibrate their bodies at the resonant frequency that causes the pollen to shoot out onto their bodies. Buzz-pollination is a prime example of the exceptionally close relationship that can evolve between flower and pollinator.

Oil-collecting bee on *Diascia cardiosepala*.

Scarab beetle on *Leucospermum tottum*.

Carpenter bee on *Orphium frutescens*.

For sunbirds and sugarbirds, nectar is a vital food source, and many nectar-producing plants have evolved tubular flowers to take advantage of bird pollination, among them some watsonias, ericas and aloes. These birds also feed on nectar from very differently shaped flowers, such as those of *Liparia splendens* and some *Protea* and *Leucospermum* species.

Insects, too, are attracted by nectar. But a remarkable fact is that the total sugar concentration, and the relative concentrations of the nectar's component sugars – sucrose, fructose and glucose – are often quite different in bird-pollinated flowers from those pollinated by insects. Butterflies are among the insects that distribute pollen in their search for nectar. The Table Mountain pride butterfly (*Aeropetes tulbaghia*) seeks out only red or orange coloured flowers and is the pollinator of a range of late-summer and autumn flowering species which includes, among many others, *Disa uniflora*, *Crassula coccinea*, *Gladiolus cardinalis*, *G. stefaniae*, *G. sempervirens*, *Cyrtanthus elatus* and *Brunsvigia marginata*. Plant species which have evolved a common characteristic to attract a specific pollinator are said to form a guild. That plants from totally unrelated families have separately evolved the same characteristic is eloquent testimony to the powerful evolutionary force of selection.

There are guilds in which the relationship between flower and pollinator is exceptionally tight. Among the more extraordinary insects at the Cape are the long-tongued flies, some of which have probosces up to 70 millimetres in length, which they use to take nectar from the bottom of very long, narrow, tubular-shaped flowers. These unusually featured flowers have co-evolved with the flies in some species of *Babiana*, *Lapeirousia*, *Pelargonium* and other genera. The plants are wholly dependent on these flies for reproduction.

A number of the region's shrubs produce seeds with a fleshy extension called an elaiosome, which has a scent that is irresistible to certain species of ants. Seeds falling to the ground are assiduously collected by the ants and taken underground to their nests, where the elaiosome is eaten, leaving the seeds safe from predators and in an ideal position for germination.

The mutual needs of plants and the animals which are their pollinators or which disperse their seeds, argues forcefully for the preservation not only of individual species but of whole, healthily functioning ecosystems.

Long-tongued fly in *Lapeirousia anceps*.

FINDING THE FLOWERS

Because of their poor soils and, sometimes inaccessibility, the mountains of the Cape Floral Kingdom still retain a substantial proportion of their natural vegetation in a more or less pristine state. Very little of the lowlands, however, has escaped the encroachment of man. Less than 5 per cent of lowland renosterveld, for instance, has survived because its relatively fertile soils have been exploited for wheat production and pasturage. The fynbos of the forelands has fared much better, with about 60 per cent of its original extent more or less undisturbed by the human presence, but much of this area is heavily infested by the alien plants that supplant the indigenous vegetation. These aliens include several Australian *Acacia* species, Australian myrtle (*Leptospermum laevigatum*), the Australian *Hakea* spp. and a variety of pines (*Pinus* spp.). The pines and hakeas are also a serious problem in the mountain fynbos.

The major threats to the remaining natural vegetation in the Cape Floral Kingdom are:

– First, public and political ignorance and indifference, which means that, in terms of government funding and support, conservation has received too low a priority rating.

– Second, aggressive and poorly controlled commercial development, particularly of the remaining natural coastline.

– Third, expansion of the land used for farming, forestry and, as the Cape's population continues to grow, urban sprawl.

– Fourth, the relentless spread of alien invasive plants.

Just under 20 per cent of the Cape Floral Kingdom falls within proclaimed nature reserves. Although this figure seems high, much of it represents mountain fynbos, of which 50 per cent of the original extent is actively conserved. Just 4,5 per cent of lowland fynbos falls within conserved areas and a pitiful 0,6 per cent of the original renosterveld area is officially protected. At present, conservation areas protect about 80 per cent of the Cape Floral Kingdom's species of

Cape of Good Hope Nature Reserve.

plants. The future of this, one of the world's botanical treasurehouses, will only be assured if the general public can be educated about its value and if this knowledge is translated into political action to ensure that effective conservation receives the necessary financial and manpower support.

For those with limited time at their disposal, the best place to see many of the Cape Flora species is Kirstenbosch National Botanical Garden, on the eastern slopes of Table Mountain. The mountain itself, the Silvermine Nature Reserve and the Cape of Good Hope Nature Reserve, the latter two on the southern Cape Peninsula, contain fynbos in excellent condition. The mountain and the two reserves were scheduled to be incorporated into a national park by the end of 1997. You can see some renosterveld flowers, as well as flowers confined to granite slopes, on Lion's Head and Signal Hill, situated on the western flank of Table Mountain.

Farther afield, there are enough places to keep flower hunters busy for the rest of their lives. Whatever the time of year you visit there will be at least some fynbos plants in bloom. By contrast, the renosterveld and strandveld flowers are at their extravagant best for just three to four weeks, mainly in August and September (depending on the locality). In a good year, the spring show around Nieuwoudtville in the North West region is memorable. So, too, are the spring flowers of the West Coast National Park. In the Tsitsikamma National Park to the east, the environment is very different: it embraces forests as well as the dense, tall coastal fynbos characteristic of the southern maritime belt.

There are some beautiful walks in the natural forest areas between George and Humansdorp. The huge protected areas managed by the conservation departments of the Western and Eastern Cape provide effectively unlimited opportunities for viewing fynbos flowers.

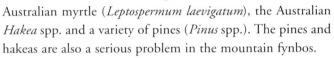

The crane-flower *Strelitzia reginae*, one of the Cape Flora's best known flowers, in cultivation at Kirstenbosch. >

INDEX OF SPECIES

Sparaxis tricolor

RECOMMENDED READING
• The Botanical Society of South Africa's series of Wild Flower Guides.
• Cowling, Richard & Richardson, Dave. *Fynbos – South Africa's Unique Floral Kingdom.* Fernwood Press. 1995.
• Cowling, R.M. (ed). *The Ecology of Fynbos - Nutrients, Fire and Diversity.* Oxford University Press. 1992. (A source book, for the academic reader and researcher.)
• Levy, Jaynee. *Complete Guide to Walks and Trails in Southern Africa.* 3rd ed., Struik Publishers. 1993.
• Bond, Pauline & Goldblatt, Peter. *Plants of the Cape Flora.* Journal of South African Botany supplementary volume no. 13. 1984. (An updated and more informative catalogue of the Cape Flora, by John Manning and Peter Goldblatt, is scheduled for publication.)

ACKNOWLEDGEMENTS

Syncarpha vestita

I count myself fortunate in the help, hospitality and companionship that I have received during the many years spent looking for and photographing the flowers of the Cape Floral Kingdom. I am especially indebted to:

My long-standing friends John Rourke and Jan Vlok, who have always been ready to share their profound knowledge of Cape plants.

Mark and Amida Johns, role-models for dedicated and interested conservationists, in whose company I have seen a great many of the Kogelberg's treasures.

Gerhard Kirsten, my companion on many a flower-hunting expedition; and Dave Osborn, whose enthusiasm is matched by his boundless energy.

John Manning and Peter Goldblatt, with whom I have experienced the excitement of some of the Cape's loveliest flowers and who have freely given of their expert knowledge of plant/insect interactions.

Peter Linder for checking the text.

Di Stafford for deciphering my writing.

Trinity Fry for her inspiring design of this book.

Dee, who has somehow managed to combine the roles of constructive critic, botanical consultant, companion and wife, and has done so with grace, patience and humour.

C. P-J